D1319274

For Jordan, who planted the seed of inspiration
—J. Marzollo

For my dear friend, Lugene
—J. Moffatt

Text copyright © 1996 by Jean Marzollo.
Illustrations copyright © 1996 by Judith Moffatt.
All rights reserved. Published by Scholastic Inc.
Printed in the U.S.A.

ISBN 0-439-69316-0

SCHOLASTIC, HELLO READER!, and associated logos and designs are trademarks and/or registered trademarks of Scholastic Inc.

1 2 3 4 5 6 7 8 9 10   23   12 11 10 09 08 07 06 05 04

I'm a Seed

by Jean Marzollo
Illustrated by Judith Moffatt

Hello Science Reader!

SCHOLASTIC INC.
New York Toronto London Auckland Sydney
Mexico City New Delhi Hong Kong Buenos Aires

I'm a seed.

I'm a seed, too!

I'm going to be a marigold
when I grow up.

Me, too!

No, you're not.

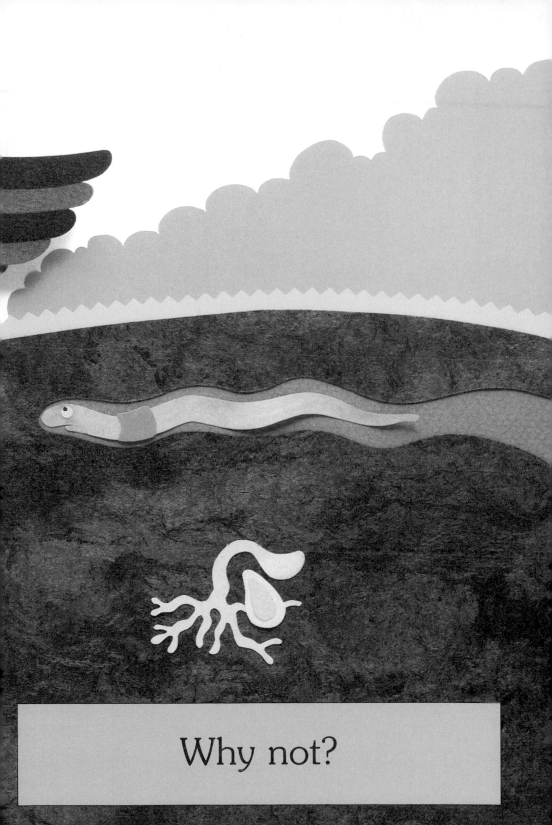

Why not?

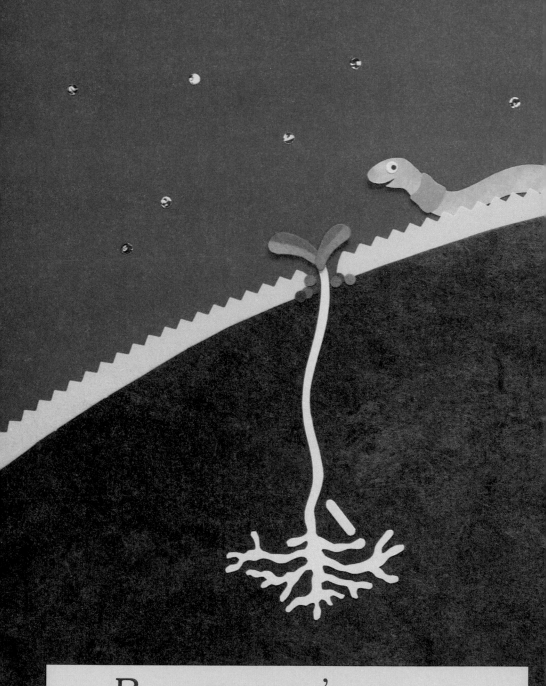

Because you're a
different kind of seed.

What kind of seed am I?

How should I know?
Wait and see.

Wait how long?

Not too long. See?
We're growing.
My stem goes up, up, up.

My stem goes sideways.

My leaves are small
and perky.

My leaves are big
and hairy.

My flowers reach up to the sky.

My flowers are hiding under my leaves.

I have **twenty** flowers!

Now I am round and orange.
What in the world am I?

A pumpkin plant!
You grew six pumpkins!
They're beautiful!

Thank you. I am very proud.

What?

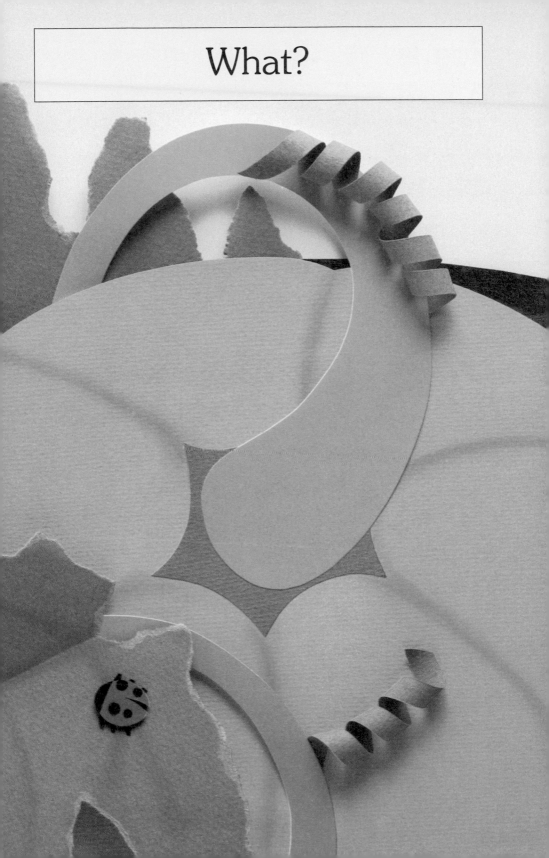

Seeds.
When my seeds are planted, they will become new marigolds.

When my seeds are planted, they will become new pumpkins.

There should be a name for it.

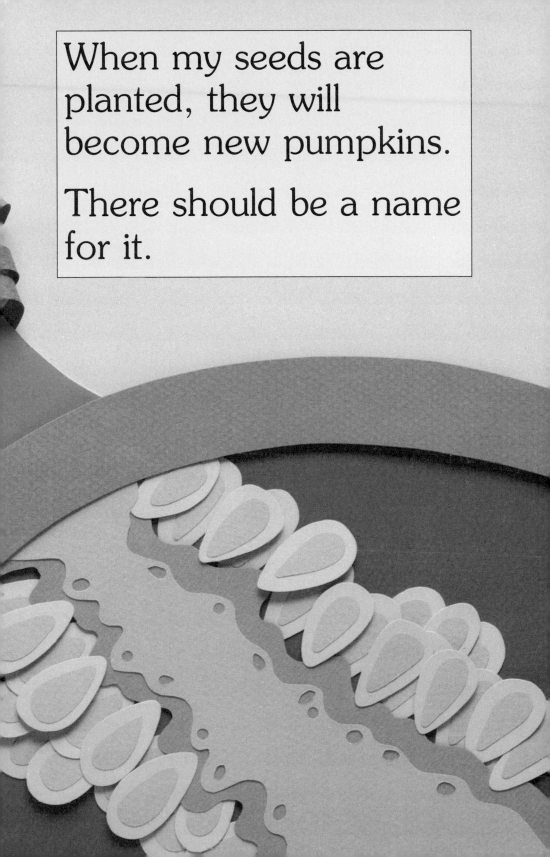

There is.
It's called life.

I'm a seed.
I'm a seed, too!